The Sound of S

(Le Bel Indifférent)

A play by
Jean Cocteau

English version by
Anthony Wood

Samuel French — London
New York - Toronto - Hollywood

CHARACTERS

The Woman
Emile, the gigolo

THE SOUND OF SILENCE
(Le Bel Indifférent)

A poor-looking, slightly seedy hotel room, lit by the neon lights from the street

There is a divan bed, a sofa, a gramophone and a telephone. There are posters on the walls. There is a small bathroom off to the side

As the Curtain *rises, the Woman is alone, wearing a little black dress*

She watches at the window, and runs to the door to listen for the lift, then comes to sit by the telephone and dials a number

Woman Hallo! ... Hallo! Is that you, Georgette? Put me on to Mr Totor. ... Yes, see if you can find him. I'll wait. ... He's there? Splendid! Put him on. What a racket! Sounds like a wild crowd. ... Why not. Totor? Is that you?... It's me. ... Yes. ... Is Emile upstairs? ... No? Have you seen him? ... When? ... Was he alone? ... Oh! Oh! I see. And you have no idea where he was going? Didn't he say anything to you? Was he drunk? Oh! I'm not worried ... It's just that I had something urgent to tell him, and I can't get hold of him. Is everything all right? ... Bravo! ... Me? I've just got back from singing. ... I'm exhausted. ... Better. Much better. ... The doctor? Do you think I have money to spend on doctors? No, I nurse myself. I come home ... and go to bed. ... Emile? Emile is an angel. He is wonderful to me. Why, yes of course he is coming home. He never leaves me on my own ... He must have had some business to attend to. Oh well, never mind. ... Thank you, Totor. ... Two o'clock in the morning? Already! How time flies. Well ... Goodbye ... goodbye, Totor. All the best!

She hangs up. She hears the lift and goes to listen at the door. The phone rings. She rushes to answer

Hallo! … Oh, it's you. Your brother? Of course your brother is here. He's here, but he's in the bathroom. I'll call him. Emile! Emile! What? … You can't come? That's charming … charming. Hallo! He is so vulgar. … No. … He yells that he is naked and that it would be indecent to come to the telephone like that. Yes, I'm sure he's there. … You're crazy, Simone. Of course he's here. I can't help it if he refuses to put himself out to come and talk to you. (*Shouting*) Your sister thinks you could make an effort … (*Into the telephone*) He really has a choice vocabulary. No, he is in the bath and says he is staying there. I'll call you back later.

She hangs up. Through clenched teeth

Bitch!

She resumes her vigil at the window. There is the noise of the lift. She rushes to the door. We hear another door open and close. Silence. She stands leaning against the door, limp and exhausted. She goes to the clock and puts the hands forward

(*In a half-voice*) It's not so difficult to call, to pick up the telephone.

She looks at the telephone and suddenly decides to put on a cloak. The sound of keys. She discards the cloak. She throws herself on the sofa and picks up a book

The door opens

Emile enters. He is a handsome gigolo, almost past it. He comes in and, during the ensuing action, undresses, whistling as he moves from the bathroom to the bedroom

Your sister phoned. I told her you were in the bath. There was no point in her knowing that you hadn't come back to the hotel. That you were out on the tiles, God knows where. That would have pleased her too much. She only called to be nosey. She kept repeating "Are you sure he's there?" What a bitch!

Where were you? I asked at Totor's. They'd seen you, but no-one knew where you were. Time passes so quickly. I was reading ... I thought I had just come back from singing. And then I looked at the clock and I saw it was an impossible hour. ... Where were you?

Silence

Terrific! You don't want to answer, as usual. Then don't answer, my good man, I won't cross-question you, keep on at you. I'm not one of those women who go in for interrogations, who follow your every footstep until they find out what they want to know. You need have no fear of that. I ask you where you were. You refuse to reply. The case is closed.

Only, in future, I'll also suit myself. I'll go wherever I like. And I won't be accountable to you. That would be too easy. Thank you very much. Monsieur does what he likes and Madame must stay locked up at the hotel. I understand. I didn't understand ... Now I understand. Good-night, ladies and gentlemen.

I am fool enough to wear myself out singing in that club full of smoke ... I come home like a good little girl to wait for his lordship ... and his lordship doesn't come home. His lordship feels quite secure. He knows that Madame is at the hotel ... that she's asleep. So his lordship does a tour of the nightclubs. Well, that's all going to change. As from tomorrow I'll accept the invitations from all the johnnies who send me flowers and notes. Champagne, dancing, the lot ... everything. Then Monsieur will see how much fun it is to wait. Always to wait.

Emile has put on his dressing-gown. He lies on the bed, lights a cigarette and holds up a newspaper, hiding his face

That's right, read your newspaper. Go on, read your newspaper, or rather pretend to read it. Nothing will stop me from saying ——

Someone bangs on the dividing wall

(*continuing more quietly*) — from saying what is on my mind. I know you're listening to me, that you're only pretending to turn a deaf ear.

It's a useful thing, a newspaper. You can hide behind a newspaper, but behind that newspaper I can guess at your wicked and attentive expression. Yes, my darling, at-ten-tive. And I will have my say ... get it all off my chest. Nothing will prevent me from doing that. Read your newspaper. Go on, read your paper. It's so easy.

Do you know what it's like to be ill, to feel drained, to have a terrible cough, to have to sing for an audience who laugh and chatter and clatter their plates? Do you know what it's like to come home ... to look forward to being close to the person you love only to find the room empty, and to have to wait?

Waiting. I know this room. Oh how I know this room. I know the red and green lights which flicker on and off, like the twitchings of an old lunatic. I know the taxis that sound as if they are going to stop, that slow down and then drive on. And each time, my heart misses a beat. I know the lift that comes up to the floor above or stops at the floor below, and the sound of the other doors opening and closing.

I know the hands of the clock which speed along when you're not watching them and, when you are watching, creep along like thieves in the night ... so stealthily that they seem not to move at all and you think the clock must be slow.

Waiting. For you, making me wait is an art, a Chinese torture. You know all the tricks, all the most excruciating ways of making every moment seem twice as long.

How I've waited. I count to a thousand, to ten thousand, to a hundred thousand. I count my steps between the window and the door. I count them forwards and backwards and every which way. I try to read a book. But all the time I listen … I listen with every fibre of my being, like the animals. And sometimes I can't contain myself and I telephone. I telephone one of those sleazy clubs where you hang out, where no doubt you torment other women. And always you have just left. And no-one ever knows where you've gone. The cloakroom girl always sounds like a mother hen, full of sympathy. Oh, I could kill her. Yes, I do believe I could kill. I might even kill you. There are cases of women who have killed their lover for less.

Waiting. Waiting. Always waiting. It's enough to drive you crazy. And it's crazy women who kill … Afterwards I'd kill myself. I couldn't bear to live without you. I'm sure of that. But what could you expect, it's a perfectly normal reaction. Who could blame me? I ask you. Listen to me, I talk and talk … anyone else would throw down the newspaper, answer me back, explain himself, slap me even. Not you! You just go on reading your paper, or pretending to. I'd give a lot to see your face behind that paper. That devilish face of yours. A face I love, and that makes me want to take a revolver and fire at it. Listen, Emile, I've given it a lot of thought. Tonight I've decided to say everything I want to say. You're used to my suffering in silence, keeping everything bottled up. Well, I'm fed up. I've had enough.

At two o' clock I promised myself, if you came in, to keep quiet, to be nice, to go to bed and pretend to have been asleep, as if you had woken me up. At ten past two, the torment of the lift and the cars had started. At a quarter past two, your sister had the sweet, clever idea of doing her bit of policing, to see if you were at the hotel, and at half past two I lost my self-control. I decided, de-ci-ded, that I would speak out and put an end to this silence. Oh, you can hold your tongue, you can read, take refuge behind your newspaper. I don't care. You can't fool me. I can see you, I can see you in spite of your newspaper. My outburst bothers you. You weren't expecting it. You'd said to yourself, "She's a victim, why not take advantage?" Well, no, no, no, I refuse to be a victim and to let myself get all in a stew. I'm going to fight, and I'm going to emerge victorious.

I love you. That's a fact. I love you, and there you have the upper hand. You profess to love me. You don't love me at all. If you loved me, Emile, you wouldn't make me wait, you wouldn't torment me every moment, trailing from club to club and leaving me to wait. I eat my heart out. I'm no more than a shadow of myself. A ghost ... just a ghost. A ghost tied up in chains, all the chains you have bound me with. A ghost locked in a dungeon.

I know what you want. I know ... you want to come and go, do whatever takes your fancy, go to bed with all the world, and know that I, who you suppposedly love, am securely locked away in a safe to which you hold the key in your pocket. That way you would be content. It's despicable. Your selfishness knows no bounds. Only you forgot that I was a woman, not a thing, that I could sing, that I was successful, that I earned my own living and that I had a whole host of people ready to defend me. All those unknown people who listen to me on the radio, who buy my records. Hah! I would only have to cry for help and they'd soon sort you out!

Emile! Oh! Right! Go on. Read your paper, read your paper. You must have finished it by now. Why don't you read it again, read it from top to bottom and from bottom to top and from left to right and from right to left. You are a monster. That's what you are. A monster. Monsieur is calm. Monsieur wants to show me how calm he is. And I? Am I not calm? You see. I am calmness personified. A positive model of tranquility. I don't know many women who would keep calm as long as I have. Anyone else would have long ago torn the newspaper away from you and forced you to give some answers. Not me. I decided to remain calm, and I have done.

It's you who have lost your cool. I'm not a fool. I can see your legs trembling and your knuckles whitening. You're consumed with rage. You're consumed with rage because you know you're in the wrong.

Where were you? I phoned Totor's, you had just left, with a tart no doubt. Probably that filthy tart you sleep with when you tell me you are with your colleagues in Marseilles. Oh, don't deny it ... I know you and I know her. I'm sure of it. A woman twice your age who gets her clothes from the flea market. Everyone turns to stare at her in the street. And that's the tart Monsieur has found. That's the tart with whom he is unfaithful to me. I would understand your being unfaithful with a fresh young girl, an inexperienced little thing who had got under your skin. I don't say it would delight me. No. But I could find excuses for you in a case like that. But this. An old bag, not even rich, who needs you to support her, and who gives you what? What? I ask you. How foolish men are. Foolish and dumb. And a disaster. Disaster. That's the word I was looking for.

And my health. Do you ever think of it, my health? You don't give a damn. If I dropped dead you'd be rid of me. Do you think it's good for my health, this waiting, waiting, always waiting. Going from that window to that door and from that door to that window. There was no telephone in this wretched hotel. I had one installed. Why? So that Monsieur could put my mind at rest, tell me: "I have some business to attend to, I am at such and such address, don't worry, my darling. I'll be coming straight back". What a waste of money. Instead, it's your sister who phones. On top of everything else, the telephone has become just another instrument of torture. There was the lift. There was the bell downstairs. There were the keys in the door. There was the clock. There was the telephone. This telephone that I watch, that I devour with my eyes. And the silence. Monsieur would never think, wherever he was, God knows where — I would rather not know — he would never think to say to himself: "She's all alone in the hotel. It's not difficult. I'll give her a call". No, that would be too much trouble, it would mean stretching out your arm, show that old tart you are with that you have someone else at home. Oh, stop being so mysterious, so stubbornly silent.

Emile. Emile. One ... two ... three. Oh, you're so obstinate. You will hang on to your newspaper. Never mind. I ... I shall go on. Because you are listening. I know you're listening and that I'm annoying you. But I've started to say my piece. So I might as well let you have the whole package. Tell you everything that's in my heart. It's like a cancer. Yes, that's what it is. A cancer that's eating away at me inside.

An enormous cancer. And I must get it out, get rid of it or it will choke me.

And there are your lies. What a liar you are! To you, telling lies is as easy as breathing. Liar, liar, liar, liar, liar, liar. You tell lies without any rhyme or reason, and non-stop. If you tell me you're going to buy a box of matches it's not true; you're going to have a glass of beer, and vice versa. To you, lying is a habit, it's a game. The other day you told me you were going to the dentist. I suspected you were not telling the truth. I waited outside your old tart's hotel and saw you come out. Don't deny it and don't swear on your mother's life. I saw you. You didn't need to tell me that story about the dentist. It's true that visiting that old tart can hardly be more agreeable than going to the dentist. But that's your concern. You do what you like. What revolts me is that you have to lie about it. You tell so many lies you get yourself all tangled up in them, you trip yourself up with your lies. You forget what you've said and it becomes an embarrassment. I assure you. So often I blush when I hear you relate things which no-one can make head or tail of. And you do it with such aplomb, such aplomb. Mind you, I'm sure you also lie to the other one, to all the others. Your life must be so full of complications it's like a nightmare.

At one time, in the beginning, I was jealous of your sleeping. I used to say to myself: "Where does he go when he sleeps? Who does he see?" And you would smile and stretch yourself like a cat, and I used to hate the people in your dreams. I often used to wake you up just to get you away from them. You enjoyed your dreams so much you were furious that I had woken you. But I couldn't bear to see the blissful expression on your face.

Now, if you sleep, I say to myself: "Peace at last. I have him here. I can make a fuss of him, cuddle up to him, touch him, look at him". I sleep very badly. In fact I hardly sleep at all. I say to myself: "He's sleeping, he's not running all over town. I have him here with me. He's mine".

Emile! I swear you will drive me to do something criminal. I swear it. Or else you will drive yourself to smash everything up and you will be the one to commit the crime, to fire the shot, to be put in prison. Imagine yourself in prison. Listen to me carefullly, Emile. I've managed to control myself so far. I've managed to keep my patience with you. Only now my patience is running out. I warn you, if in three minutes ... Now, I'm going to count to thirty, if you don't put down that newspaper, I warn you I'm going to do something drastic.

She counts up to twenty-four out loud. At twenty-four the telephone rings

Saved by the bell. How lucky for you. (*Answering the telephone*) Hallo! Hallo! Hallo! Who's calling? ... No, it is not Monsieur Emile. Monsieur Emile is reading his newspaper. Ah! Ah! Ah! It's you. Yes. ... Perfectly. Just a moment. (*Her hand over the mouthpiece; to Emile*) Will you deign to answer? It's your old tart.

Silence

She's asking for you.

Silence

(*Into the telephone*) No, madame. I ... told him it was you. He refuses to be disturbed. ...I told you, he is reading his newspaper. (*Loudly*) Emile, are you coming or not? (*Into the telephone*) No. It's no —— But, Madame, there's nothing I can do. ... Really? Really? How charming. He refuses to speak to you, what do you expect me to do about it? ... Oh! (*She hangs up*) Slut!

She goes towards Emile

Thank you, Emile. That was very kind. I never thought you would be so kind. I would have died of shame if you'd spoken to that creature. Emile ... I'm a bore. I admit it ... Forgive me ...

She moves the newspaper aside. Emile is asleep, his cigarette has fallen from his mouth

He's asleep! Isn't that just typical. And here I was getting all soft, thinking …

She shakes him

Emile. Emile. Emile. You've dozed off. Wake up.

He turns over. She goes round to the other side of the bed

I was talking to you and you were asleep. Your old tart phoned. Your old tart. I thought you were refusing to stir yourself to speak to her … Emile.

Emile pushes her away brusquely. He stretches, gets up, lights a cigarette and goes towards the bathroom. She follows him. He starts to get dressed again

Emile. Are you going out? You can't do that. I'll throw myself out of the window. I'll kill myself.

She opens the window and throws out his cigarette butt

Emile goes into the bathroom without her seeing him

She leaves the window and, seeing the room empty, goes crazy

Where are you, Emile? Emile. Emile.

He comes out of the bathroom

Oh! I was frightened. I couldn't see you. I thought you'd gone.

He combs his hair

But … Emile … What are you doing? What is it? You are dressed.

He puts on his jacket

You're not going out? That's impossible. Didn't you hear what I just said? Emile, answer me ... say something ... don't be so callous, so cruel. You at least owe me an explanation. I wait ... I wait ... I wait until I'm bursting. Finally you arrive. I want to talk to you ... I talk to you but you immerse yourself in your newspaper. And you fall asleep. What then? You haven't even heard what I was saying to you. It's too much. It's as if you are cross with me and are punishing me ... but for what?

She clings to him. He pushes her aside and does up his jacket

Listen, Emile, I realize I have been a bit rough on you, that you can't stand to hear the truth ... at least about certain things which annoy you. Emile ... Emile ... Emile ... say something. Speak to me. Open your mouth. Don't stand there like a piece of granite, a statue.

He puts on his coat

What are you doing? Why are you putting on your coat? Oh no! You're not going out again. Haven't I suffered enough? I won't let you go. Have pity on me. Don't be so heartless. Emile, you do have a heart. You love me. If you didn't love me you wouldn't bother to come back here at all. But you do come back. You come in late, but you do come back. Because you care about me. Because everything is not finished between us. Speak. Swear to me that we are not finished.

Emile goes to the telephone and dials a number. She clings to his arm

Emile. You have no right to do this to me. After all I've done for you. No ... No ... I didn't mean to say that. I meant to say: after all we've meant to each other. Of course, I know that I have done nothing for you ... that there was nothing I could do ... if I did the least thing, it was only natural.

Forgive me. I'll be good. I won't complain. I'll be silent. There ... there ... I'll be quiet. I'll put you to bed and tuck you in. You'll go to sleep. And I'll watch over you as you sleep. You'll dream, and in your dreams you will go wherever you please, be unfaithful to me with whomever you please ... But stay ... stay ... stay. I would die if I had to wait for you tomorrow, and the next day.

Emile opens the door. She clings to him

It's too much. Emile, I beg you. Stay ... Look at me ... I will accept everything. You can tell lies, lies, lies. You can keep me waiting. I will wait. I will wait as long as you like.

Emile pushes her away and goes out, slamming the door

She runs to the window as——

—— the CURTAIN *falls*

FURNITURE AND PROPERTY LIST

On stage: Divan bed. *Beside it*: ashtray. *On it*: cloak, **Emile**'s
              dressing-gown
              Sofa. *On it*: book
              Gramophone
              Telephone
              Posters on walls
              Clock
              Practical window

Personal: **Emile**: cigarettes, lighter, newspaper, comb

LIGHTING PLOT

Property fittings required: nil

Interior. The same scene throughout

To open: Neon lighting effect through window

No cues

EFFECTS PLOT